HUGH HAYNIE : Perspective

5—-

D1240286

"Oh, yes sir. They're very nice moon rocks, thank you, sir."

2 February 1971

Sigma Delta Chi Distinguished Service
Award (1971)

HUGH HAYNIE : Perspective

The Courier-Journal
THE LOUISVILLE TIMES

1974

Executive Editor
Samuel W. Thomas

Editor
William S. Butt

Book Design
Julius Friedman and Nathan Felde
Images, Louisville, Kentucky

Copyright©1974
The Courier-Journal and *The Louisville Times*
525 W. Broadway, Louisville, Ky. 40202
All rights reserved including the right of
reproduction in whole or in part, in any form.

All drawings in this book were published
originally in *The Courier-Journal* and since
5 July 1972 have been copyrighted © 1972,
1973, 1974 by *The Courier-Journal.* Hugh
Haynie cartoons published in *The Courier-
Journal* between 30 June 1964 and 4 July
1972 were copyrighted © 1964, 1965,
1966, 1967, 1968, 1969, 1970, 1971, 1972
and distributed by *The Los Angeles Times*
Syndicate which continues to be the
exclusive distributor of Hugh Haynie
cartoons.

Library of Congress Catalog Number:
74-17819
Printed by the Pinaire Lithographing
Corporation, Louisville, Kentucky

First Printing
November 1974

*For my bunky, Sam Haynie, who will probably
never read this book.*

Contents

"Now, Let's See, Have I Forgotten Anyone?"

Preface

Following the appearance of a biting Hugh Haynie cartoon, the Readers' Views page of *The Courier-Journal* invariably bristles with opinion from both his advocates and adversaries. Although Haynie is sometimes perplexed by the intensity of the outcry and the distracting verbal abuses, the response justifies his demanding and often-maligned assignment. For Haynie does not try to mold public opinion; he expresses his own, and hopefully in doing so, that of the publisher. "By expressing my opinion perhaps others will search their own, and if I cause one other person to think and examine his own views, then there is a reason for doing what I do and the way I do it." Obviously many readers have been challenged by Haynie, and their positive response has fostered this Haynie anthology. The recent change in presidential administrations provides a natural time for its appearance.

"Caricatures are often the truest history of the times," Emerson once said, and we believe this, too, of our editorial cartoonist's work during his tenure at *The Courier-Journal*. Haynie, however, is not just content to mirror the times; he looks for faults in people and flaws in institutions. Like his idol, the late Walt Kelly, he feels that the editorial cartoonist should be society's watchdog, growling warnings at the first sign of trouble. Haynie admits he "tends to hit rather hard." But this is because he harbors no illusions about mankind. He is a realist, an independent observer who must look for the best and worst in all things. "I feel that it is not only the prerogative but indeed the duty of

the cartoonist to find fault," he says, "if indeed there is fault to be found." No fairy tales cloud the Haynie outlook. "In real life things don't happen that way. And I suppose because of this there will always be cartoonists."

Haynie considers himself something of an anachronism when comparing his style to that of the so-called "new school" of cartoonists. "Editorial cartooning has changed radically in the last few years," he is quick to point out, "and I still use the old stereotypes that are perhaps far too shopworn. But I rather like the 'old chestnuts' and honestly would not know how to do without them."

Yet the unique quality of Haynie's style permits him to handle a multitude of situations and events that cannot be tackled by the new breed. While demonstrably successful in their milieu, they sometimes fall short when obliged to deal with matters that do not accommodate themselves to situation comedy. Not many cartoonists can deal with tragedy as well as humor with equal facility and impact. It is a tribute to Haynie that he can fit style to circumstance, mood to event. He can be equally successful depicting a social ill as with an obituary or the spirit of Christmas.

Like most cartoonists, he believes the idea is the essential element of the cartoon. Rollin Kirby used to say that a cartoon was 75 per cent idea and 25 per cent drawing. Haynie concurs: "A poor drawing may hurt an idea, but even a superior drawing cannot enhance a badly conceived idea." Few cartoonists consider their space in the newspaper a showcase for draftsmanship. They merely try to communicate their understanding of a situation to their readership in the most effective manner possible. What the cartoon says is always more important than how it looks on the editorial page.

In the sixteen years that Haynie has been *The Courier-Journal*'s editorial cartoonist, he has regularly produced six cartoons a week, fifty weeks a year. Of these approximately 4,500 cartoons, unfortunately only 287 could be displayed in this volume.

Which raises the question: How, indeed, does one determine that one cartoon is better than another? The implication from choosing "good" cartoons is that there are "bad" cartoons, a conclusion that no cartoonist wants to hear, even though he knows that, in the daily grind, some come out better than others. Although cartooning is an endeavor in which good and bad are relative, and judgment is subjective, the selection of these cartoons was, for the most part, an objective process. This book is intended to be historical in nature, a treatment of national and international events, as seen through the eyes of Hugh Haynie. The cartoons gathered in the editors' net depict the extra-ordinary events of the past decade and a half, and they stand out from the others by the sheer weight of their content. Style was not sacrificed in the selection; exceptional events seem to bring out the best in Haynie. The cartoons that did not deal with major events, but were included, survived the battles of opinion between the editors, Haynie, and any observer within shouting range. Everyone has favorite Haynie

cartoons, including Haynie, who sat in on many planning sessions for critical purposes and also to make certain his personal favorites were selected.

It became evident, on perusing his entire collection, how dependent Haynie is upon the president (both the man and the office) as a vehicle to chronicle national events. The cartoonist's craft necessarily involves shooting at someone, preferably someone immediately recognizable and politically potent. Hence, the president makes a good target. But it is not just expediency that draws cartoonists to presidents. Cartoonists like Haynie deal in symbols. The presidency is the symbol of country, the embodiment of so many characteristics considered American. Even after the onslaught of the past year, the office holds no less fascination and interest to the public. The past four presidents made an imprint upon our lives, and consequently, upon Haynie's cartoons. Each man had a different personality which produced a tone, a backdrop, and sometimes even a catalyst for events in this country. For this reason we have arranged this book into four sections: the Eisenhower Years, the Kennedy Years, the Johnson Years, and the just-concluded Nixon Years.

This book is a museum of Haynie cartoons. The diversity of subject matter, when reviewed, presents a fascinating pictorial diary — a history of our time from the last years of Eisenhower to the present. These cartoons represent a distillation of sixteen years of major news stories, events as diverse as life can make them, all filtered through the unique perspective of one man.

Introduction

Oh that I dared
To basket up the family of plagues
That waste our vitals; peculation, sale
Of honour, perjury, corruption, frauds
By forgery, by subterfuge of law,
By tricks and lies...
Then cast them, closely bundled, every brat
At the right door!
William Cowper (1785), slightly misquoted
by the radical pamphleteer, William Hone (1821).

And what shall we name this land?
Hugh Haynie (1973), disembarking with elegant
formality and Olympian reserve from a very
modest sightseeing vessel — to the considerable
mystification of a small audience of tourists
queued up for the next departure on a fog-bound,
rain-swept public dock.

As far back as 1753, William Hogarth observed
with a certain resignation that "the inexplicable word
Humour hath been hammer'd at in all ages and yet
remains undetermined." The same might be said of
efforts to arrive at a simple, serviceable description of
that bundle of licenses and disciplines which we have
come to call the editorial cartoon.

The basic pattern for this "delivery system" was
established in 1756 when an English nobleman,
George Townshend, fused the Italian tradition of
exaggerated *caricatura* portraits with an earlier
northern European taste for pictorial polemics.
Townshend's wicked, witty little satires — scarcely
larger than playing cards — took London by storm.
Over the next three generations, Townshend and a
group of equally mutinous, more talented disciples
demonstrated the possibilities and limits of this new
mode of communication. Under the etching needles of
Gillray, Rowlandson, and George Cruikshank, the
modern cartoon took shape: a volatile compound of
intellect and emotion, outrage and entertainment,
involvement and detachment, synthesis and catharsis.
It is, in most of its higher trajectories, necessarily a
weapon of attack, an instrument of lightning clarification that takes the problem by surprise.

The caricature of individuals (or situations) is an
art of inquiry and suggestion which asks a good deal
of the viewer and a great deal of the artist. Although it
has been argued that selection and distortion ought to
be simple and affirmative responses to the invitations
of nature, the process is obviously easier put to nega-
tive purposes than positive. As Hogarth pointed out,
"It is strange that nature hath afforded us so many
lines and shapes to indicate the deficiencies and
blemishes of the mind, whilst there are none at all to
point out the perfections of it beyond the appearance
of common sense and placidity." An instinct for savage
satire is apt to hesitate and stumble if obliged to deal
with great achievement, honest sentiment or searing
tragedy. In many cases the truest test of a man's
courage and self-assurance lies in the grace with
which he can offer a rose or shed a tear.

Perhaps we respond to the daily performance of
an independent and original cartoonist with some of

the electric fascination which we feel for an aerialist on the high wire. He balances, he dares; he weighs anger against compassion, freedom against responsibility, the abstract against the particular. The process is a continuing contradiction in terms, a pursuit of truth by way of illusion. Many times the cartoonist will measure success in terms of his ability to conceal the amount of effort actually involved, only to be rewarded by the cocktail party question: "What on earth do you fellows do with the *rest* of your day?"

One of Hugh Haynie's most illustrious predecessors in Louisville, Fontaine Fox, later ringmaster of the "Toonerville Trolley," recalled his professional debut at the turn of the century:

It was breakfast time on a Sunday morning and I was descending the stairs with my chest out, chin up, shoulders back and diaphragm quite distended with pride. On this particular morning the front page of the *Herald* was to carry my first published cartoon. It was wonderful, and as if to complete the satisfaction of the moment, I saw that my father was in the living room looking at the front page. ...My father was a judge and wrote editorials for the Louisville *Courier* at a desk beside that of Colonel Henry Watterson, who was his close friend. As a consequential journalist, my father therefore, might be expected to express an opinion on my work that would be valuable. I halted for a minute and heard him explode: "All I have to say is it's a mighty queer way to make a living."

As previously intimated, this "queer" profession rises from a good many disparate roots. Before the tag end of the sixteenth century, the postmasters of Europe served as a rudimentary intelligence-gathering and distribution service. The circulation of printed news bulletins began in earnest during the early years of the seventeenth century. The first known newspaper printed in English was an untitled, single-sheet, two-page affair published at Amsterdam on 2 December 1620. (The historic opening sentence was a chaste regret that *The new tydings out of Italie are nt yet com.*) The Dutch led the way in both letterpress communication and pictorial satire. It is significant that the first important English "cartoon," *Invented by Samuel Ward preacher of Ipswich* would be *Imprinted at Amsterdam* the following year. (This was *The Double Deliveraunce,* an expression of graditude to the Almighty for the national escape from the Spanish Armada and Guy Fawkes — timed to complicate plans for a projected wedding between the Spanish infanta and Charles, Prince of Wales.) The same year, 1621, a John Hayney settled in Virginia. This gentleman may or may not have been kin to Hugh — however, the John *Haynie* who sat as a member of the House of Burgesses for Northumberland County at mid-century is demonstrably the father of the clan. Of Captain John Haynie the 1st, it suffices for the moment to point out that his only recorded act as a legislator was a signature 13 April 1652 on an oath of allegiance to the Commonwealth; an act urged on the Royalist burgesses by Cromwell's gunboats anchored off Jamestown.

Curiously enough, Oliver Cromwell's vigilance in the field (1649-53) was accompanied at home by a spirit of cautious toleration for freedom of the press. In 1649 and 1650 a mischievous Royalist weekly, *The Man in the Moon,* laid an earthy (if not downright scurrilous) foundation for the profession of satirical journalism. The *Moon's* instigator, balladeer and smutmonger John Crouch, was closed down briefly, only to return in 1652 as proprietor of an even livelier publication, *Mercurius Democritus.* This was a largely apolitical mix of inspired pornography, burlesque, and parody, brightened sporadically by random woodcuts. Crouch promised to communicate *many strange Wonders, Out of the World in the Moon, The Antipodes, Maggy* [Whimsey] — *Land, Tenebris* [realms of darkness], *Fary-Land, Green-land and other adjacent Countries* to aid the *right understanding of all the Mad-merry-People of Great Bedlam.* Pictorial matter had first been introduced to illustrate text in 1643, or in 1638, depending on how rigidly one cares to define the term "English newspaper." Crouch was probably stimulated in the spring of 1653 by the example of George Horton, who dressed up his sister weeklies *Moderate Occurrences* and *The Faithful Post* with a variety of plates and something approaching modern headlines. Topical comment, let alone polemics, became progressively more risky as the permissiveness of the Commonwealth congealed under the Protectorate (1653-58). After *Mercurius Democritus* was finally extinguished in February 1654,

Crouch continued his ribald, pre-Swiftean gambols for another year or so under the masthead of *Mercurius Fumigosus Or The Smoking Nocturnall.*

This early flowering, or festering, of the spirit of caricature was not rivaled or approximated until the dawn of the eighteenth century. The spark was sustained, after a fashion, by the random production of single-sheet visual satires, hamfisted "emblems" or "hieroglyphs" which were invariably Dutch in manner and often Dutch in execution. Humor did not begin to insinuate itself into this genre until the 1720s. Young William Hogarth's initial experiments were firmly rooted in the grand allegorical tradition, yet with a difference. His telescopic fantasy of 1724 identifies a trio of surreal establishment blockheads (Monarchy, Episcopacy, and Law) as *Some of the Principal Inhabitants of ye Moon…(Exactly engraved… whereby ye Curious may Guess at their Religion, Manners, &c.)* — a polished celestial artifice with strong overtones of John Crouch and Jonathan Swift. Hogarth affected a majestic disdain for the rough and tumble of personal caricature, which he appeared to regard as trivial and bitchy. *Think not to find one meant Resemblance there,* he inscribed beneath a print of 1733, *We lash the Vices but the Persons spare.* Hogarth's sturdy bourgeois example, his successful establishment of a printmaker's copyright act (1735), his flair for promotion, and, hardly least, his unique mix of genius and British independence, united to convert the precarious, servile craft of "popular" printmaking into both profession and industry. He would, however, have been strongly tempted to deck any foolhardy prophet who informed him that he was destined for canonization as the patron saint of the cartoon.

It may be irresponsible to suggest that two vital non-Hogarthian ingredients — intellectual caprice and personal malice — fall naturally into the province of the aristocracy. Nevertheless, during the next century, Lord Townshend and a host of well-born imitators and followers provided the new art with an invaluable cross-fertilization of sophistication, impudence, and inside dope. This amateur vogue was cannily developed and marketed by Townshend's publishers, Matthew and Mary Darly. Anthologies of their tiny "caricaturas" were knowingly promoted as having been "Drawn and Etched by some of the most eminent Parties Interested Therein"; potential clients were assured that any "Sketches or Hints, sent Post paid… will have due Honour shewn them." One measure of the appeal thus exerted is supplied by Mary Darly's *Book of Caricaturas,* a diminutive how-to-do-it volume published in December 1762 "For the Use of Young Gentlemen and Ladies." This work consisted of a title page, two pages of text and fifty-seven engraved "samples." Mrs. Darly describes the practice as a *burlesque of Character or an exaggeration of nature, when not very pleasing, its a manner of drawing that was & still is held in great esteem by both the Italians & French. Some of our Nobility & Gentry,* she adds, *at this time do equal if not excel any thing of the kind that ever has been done in any other country*…Her other page of text consisted of one long sentence of

instruction and an admonition to *keep constantly practicing from this book till drawing in this manner becomes familiar & is attended with pleasure.*

As caricature printmaking acquired a degree of professionalism toward the century's end, the innovative role of the amateur tended to diminish. The cycle would start anew on this side of the Atlantic in later days when fledgling comic papers began their desperate fights for survival. The first number of *The Lantern* (10 January 1852), conducted by "Diogenes the Younger," addressed itself to "the wielders of pen and pencil in these here United States":

> Bretheren — You are hereby notified and, indeed, solicited to correspond with us, not only in matter but in manner, to enrich the blaze of our Weekly Luminary — bearing in mind that refined Wit, without personality, and Comic illustrations, without vulgarity, are indispensable.
>
> The Subjects, which may consist of Rough Sketches on Paper or written suggestions of a Local Character, will, as they are sent in, undergo a proper criticism, and those which are approved of and used, will be paid for, *if required.* [My italics.]

Useful amateur input was only one of the key components which helped to create the rambunctious "golden age" of English caricature, 1775-1815. Georgian printsellers also were abetted by a rising enthusiasm for disruptive comment, a climate of increasing journalistic latitude and resourcefulness, an appetite for illustration of all sorts, and by the general artistic stimulus provided through the foundation of the Royal Academy and its training schools (1768). The prevailing tone was skeptical, outrageous, and anti-establishment, even though satirical prints were comparatively expensive commodities, and the shops that sold them were, by and large, a sort of kept entertainment for the upper classes. The preoccupation with respectability and good manners (witness *The Lantern*) would come later, along with editors, editorial policies, Victorian sensibilities and spiraling circulations.

By the early 1800s the cartoon had come into its own as an instrument of propaganda: personal, economic, and official. The etcher's needle was available for advertisement and detraction. London mercantile and banking interests bombarded revolutionary Holland with trilingual satires in 1796, producing no visible result. The following year, British government officials arrived at a serviceable understanding — classified by some as a bribe — with the foremost caricaturist of the day, James Gillray. Prime Minister Pitt helped his junior ministers edit a polemical weekly. George Canning, future premier, directed a flow of "hints and suggestions" to Gillray. Across the Channel, Emperor Napoleon commanded (30 May 1805) his Minister of Police to

Have caricatures made: An Englishman, purse in hand, entreating the various powers to take his money, &c. This is the real direction to give the whole business; and the huge care the English are taking to gain time by spreading false news,

all the symptoms together, prove its extreme importance.

If there was a point to be put (or a boom to be lowered), chances were that an artist could be engaged to do the job. A nadir of sorts was achieved during the "Queen's Affair" (1820) when some mercenary English printmakers elected to crank out attacks on George IV, in limited editions of one or two, solely for the purpose of having them expensively suppressed by their intended victim. None of this did much for the general reputation of the trade, and it probably helps to explain why the old school of caricaturists, and caricature itself, was regarded with distaste by fair-minded Victorians.

An article in *The Athenaeum* (1 October 1831) compared James Gillray to a caterpillar on the "green leaf of reputation — who loved to crawl over those fame had marked out as her own." Gillray's profession was described as "bastard painting intended to vilify the human form and render its actions ridiculous":

[The Caricaturist] neither reverences domestic peace, nor dreads the vengeance of public assemblies, and though he is generally regarded as a nuisance, who for his audacious pictures deserves the pillory, he is permitted to walk at large by the courtesy of government and our love of fun and freedom.

The same author winds up with the observation that physical peculiarities — Pitt's nose and "grasshopper legs," Fox's corpulence, Napoleon's stature — are the only parts of those statesmen on which sordid caricature "fixed her canker tooth." "Yet," he concludes, "the high vulgar and the low laugh as they idle through the streets. It saves them the trouble of reading and also the expense of thought."

A similar well-bred resistance to the practice was solidly entrenched in the United States, where the real thing had barely been tried. The original Italian word *caricare* meant "to load or charge," presumably with meaning, or better yet, with "Truth." On 19 July 1866 E. L. Godkin's prestigious journal, *The Nation,* devoted a lengthy editorial to its view of the problem, arguing in part:

> The essence of caricature is exaggeration to deformity, and however it may entertain us, there is always the drawback of its untruthfulness.... Humor is not usually a quality of virtuous indignation; and great immoralities, public or private, are not to be dealt with in a spirit of levity, because to subject them to the ordeal of ridicule, would be really to diminish the abhorrence with which they should be regarded. ... The tendency of caricature is to license, and this in turn to vulgarity. ... There may be power in the talent so exercised, but it is the same power which resides in the pistol of the house-breaker or the bludgeon of the highwayman. A good man is not likely to possess it and will certainly be incapable of using it. ... The decline of caricature as a means of personal attack [compared with the days of Gillray] may be considered as a mark of advancing refinement. ...

One year later (1867), ignoring this solemn warning, the *New York Evening Telegram* became the first daily newspaper in the country to run cartoons on a regular basis, offering a large front-page design every Friday. (Godkin evidently remained unconvinced. A generation later he angrily pitched a series of Thomas Nast's cartoons out of his *Evening Post* on the ground that they represented a "lowering of the character" of the paper.)

Good, gentle Murat Halstead had started a paper called the *Extra* in the Spring of '84, and he bought some of my cartoons...I met "Marse Henry" Watterson in the *Extra* office one day, and he offered me a job on his Louisville paper but I had seen the Southwest and felt that it was too roughnecked and coarse for a refined devotee of the Pure.

When I maladroitly hinted at my reason for refusing his offer, Mr. Watterson...stated his opinion that New York was the meanest, tightest, coldest-hearted, rottenest, foulest, vilest and most God-forsaken city since Babylon, each of these adjectives being festooned and garnished with Kentucky swear words meaning "damn," oaths that snapped and sparkled like exploding meteors.
Walt McDougall (1858-1938) in his 1926 autobiography, *This is the Life!*

**Things have come to a hell of a pass
When a man can't whip his own jackass.**
Colonel Watterson in defense of editorial freedom, couplet of uncertain date.

The first professional caricaturist to commence operations in the United States seems to have been an enterprising, moderately-talented Englishman named William Charles (1776-1820). At twenty-two, Charles was advertising his services as a "quick sketch artist" in the London press. By 1805 he was proprietor of "Charles's Emporium of Art and Fancy Produce" in Edinburgh, a situation the artist appears to have vacated in haste — just ahead of the law — to settle in New York. He issued some three dozen political prints in the Gillray manner there and in Philadelphia, where he spent the last several years of his life. A second artist, far more competent than Charles, worked briefly (1808-9) — in this country — under the pseudonym "Peter Pencil," and one assumption would be that he went to England as relations between the two countries slipped towards war. (William Heath, active in London from 1809 to 1834, later employed the pen name "Paul Pry," and might well have been the same individual.)

On this tentative foundation the American cartoon gradually evolved from etching to lithograph to woodcut, from broadside to almanac to weekly. The development of photo-mechanical reproduction in the 1860s and 70s made daily newspaper cartoons a practical possibility, although the expense of line engraving was such that cheaper do-it-yourself alternatives like "chalk plate" were still in wide use at the turn of the century.

In June 1884 Joseph Pulitzer broke new ground, appointing a self-assured free-lancer from Newark as staff cartoonist of the New York *World*. The day before, Walt McDougall impulsively dumped a "rather ambitious cartoon on James G. Blaine," the Republican nominee for president, into the hands of an elevator boy at the *World*. McDougall's cartoon had been rejected by the magazine *Puck,* and he remembered not wanting to lug it to a baseball game. "Give that to the editor and tell him he can have it if he wants it," McDougall stammered. In the very best Horatio Alger fashion, McDougall arose the next morning to find a waiting telegram from Pulitzer and his cartoon spread across five columns of page one. "I was twenty-six years old, weighed a hundred and fifty-five at the ringside, and the *World* was mine. ..." On 30 October 1884 McDougall helped to elect Grover Cleveland with a celebrated cartoon: *The Feast of Belshazzar Blaine and the Money Kings.* The transplant was taking.

It is fascinating to speculate on what might have transpired if "Marse Henry" Watterson had managed to recruit McDougall for *The Courier-Journal* the previous spring. Except for the occasional insertion of a small woodcut, *The Courier-Journal's* founder and editor hardly could have been more conservative in matters of design and typography. The thought of his stealing a march on the innovative Pulitzer is especially seductive. The fact that Watterson began to publish cartoons by a Louisvillian named Goodall in October 1884 suggests indeed he was taking the matter seriously. *The Courier-Journal* experimented with cartoons over the next four decades. In 1888 particular use was made of the work of Thomas Nast — a Watterson friend — and of a local man who signed himself "Mc." After 1900 there was an increase in reprints from other papers and in material obtained by syndication. The cartoons of Hearst's star cartoonist, Homer Davenport, appeared with some frequency.

Over the years there were a number of hometown "temporary regulars," but none appears to have enjoyed the status of staff editorial cartoonist prior to Watterson's retirement as editor in August 1918. (Since that time there have been only two such cartoonists: Grover Page, who held the post from 1919 to 1958, and Hugh Haynie.)

In retrospect it is not surprising that Henry Watterson failed to find, or employ a permanent cartoonist during the half century that *The Courier-Journal* was under his control. The courageous, controversial paper which he created in November 1868 had always been something of a one-man show. Its editorial page, the heart and mind of the operation, was dominated by Watterson's own views. These were presented with force, wit, bite, grace, subtlety, clarity, elegance, and elaboration. They also tended to run long, often three columns or better. The prospect of strong competition in the opinion field might not have been entirely agreeable to Watterson. Cartoons by a malleable yes-man for any extended period would have been unacceptable to him. He may well have shared some of E. L. Godkin's feelings concerning the limitations of caricature. His lengthy and affectionate obituary editorial on Thomas Nast (11 December 1902) masks a few reservations about dealing with "artistic" types under the digressive guise of a tribute to Nast's publisher, Fletcher Harper. Watterson marvelled at Harper's "keen insight" into the "idiosyncracies of the craft and the strange requirements of its votaries":

...the temperamental strength and infirmities of

that sometimes emotional and sometimes stoical brotherhood which is alternately puerile and sublime, fanciful and heroic.... .

Significantly, almost a third of the Nast obit is devoted to praise of Harper. Watterson did salute Nast's "exquisite touch, his vivid, trained poetic imagination," and his "severe, introspective self-discipline":

He drew with a bold hand and a doughty spirit. His satire flashed upon a rogue and discovered a rascal like a policeman's lantern. Always unsparing and direct, sometimes cruel, he was the old Saxon warrior... .

One suspects that Henry Watterson would have appreciated Hugh Haynie. They could have shared a mutual enthusiasm for good conversation, vintage anecdotes, fine food and drink, and intense likes and dislikes. It may be just as well, however, that they never had a chance to work on the same editorial page.

Writing in the mid-twenties, Walt McDougall spoke of his youth as the "Neolithic Period" of newspaper art and of himself and his contemporaries as "Cro-Magnon draftsmen." "Nevertheless," he continued, "although forty years have passed, newspaper illustration in general remains almost as crude." Like the England of Townshend and Gillray, one mark of progress was the arrival of the how-to-do-it brigade. From 1910 to 1930 the shrill pitch of the cartoon correspondence school reverberated across the land. With the number of job opportunities rapidly rising, a dozen or more establishments were working the field by the end of World War I. There were tempting offers of "free equipment" and a proliferation of testimonials from satisfied, and presumably affluent, former pupils. The Federal School of Applied Cartooning in Minneapolis advertised that their "Twenty-seven Stars" would teach you just about anything. A full-page ad in *Cartoons Magazine* for December 1917 celebrated the success of Grover Page, then of the *Nashville Tennessean,* who had learned his trade from the Evans School of Cartooning in Cleveland, while an electrician in Gastonia, North Carolina. (He writes: "It did *wonders* for me and will do as much for anyone who takes it and puts forth a little energy.") A book on "Chalk Talks" and the offer of "A Whole Bundle of Original Cartoons for $1.00" were pushed separately in the same issue, each with an ecstatic letter from G. H. Yuhas of Bridgeport, Connecticut, proclaiming their respective worths as training aids.

The apparent captain of this industry was C. N. Landon of Cleveland. From humble beginnings in or about 1912, The Landon Course had expanded by 1924 to a regimen of at least forty-six separate lessons dealing with everything from "Shadows" to "Wrinkles." Each of these, packaged in a small folio, consisted of text, instructions, and pictorial examples. Mr. Landon's chapter (1914) on "Symbolical Figures" supplies a bit of general advice before he gets down to the blueprint for Uncle Sam. An individual labeled "Common People" represents the "everyday American Citizen"; another, "The Trusts," stands for "the combinations of big business."

As a rule [Landon continues] Russia, Spain, Holland, Germany, Canada and other nations are represented by a figure wearing the costume of that particular country. Cuba and the Central American countries are represented by a little, delapidated colored boy, generally with a knife or a gun about his person, ready for revolution.

An equally enlightening Landon foray (1921) concerns "Serious Cartoons":

There are some topics, however, which cannot be expressed in a humorous way. Cartoon ideas based on political graft, crusades against officials who do not enforce the law, disputes between capital and labor, the evils of Bolshevism, etc. require serious treatment. ...First we will take up the figures used in drawing Serious Cartoons. The figure of a woman is sometimes used to represent the United States. She is called "Columbia" ...

The accompanying illustrative matter includes several patterns for the Long Arm of the Law, an omnibus specter of "Hunger, Starvation, Anarchy *or* Bolshevism," a grandfatherly gent in eighteenth-century dress who will serve for "Philadelphia, Pittsburgh, New York [or] Cleveland" and some marvelous skeletons (grimly reaping, beckoning, accusing, swallowing armies, glowering in closets and the like).

By the mid-twenties the nation's editors were leaning toward the light touch in cartoons, conceivably in reaction to the horrific diet of war demons and revolutionary furies served up during the previous decade. The reigning masters tended to be warm-hearted and gentlemanly, like John T. McCutcheon and "Ding" Darling. In his book *How to Draw Cartoons* (1926), Clare Briggs expresses satisfaction that the cartoonist as scourge had been replaced by the cartoonist as educator:

...With the growing complexity of our social order, the cartoonist has sought to explain the essentials of an intricate issue by a simple picture. It is now more a matter of laughing "with" the characters presented than "at" them....

We live in a world that is largely run by precedent and tradition. There is force in the idea that what has happened before will happen again. The belief that you cannot depart from certain time-honored and revered rules without courting disaster is widely held. Therefore it is essential that the cartoonist shall know what has happened before — history. He must know something of the big moments in the life of our heroes, because one of the most effective means of driving home an idea is to show that it was sponsored by our venerated forebears.

This beneficent age of amiable uplift, noble clarification and rampant labeling was to endure, more or less intact for a quarter-century, despite the best efforts of such iconoclasts as Daniel Fitzpatrick, Rollin Kirby, Edmund Duffy, and Herbert L. Block — who began drawing for the Chicago *Daily News* in 1929 when Hugh Haynie was two.

As recently as 1960, cartoonists from abroad were

inclined to echo Walt McDougall's earlier feeling about the Neolithic status of editorial caricature in the United States, particularly when contrasted with the much-admired achievements of *The New Yorker* and Walt Disney in other areas. Just as some historians finally were waking up to the value of the cartoon as a serious tool of historical research, others were claiming that it had outlived its contemporary usefulness and ought to be scrapped.

The ideal would be to be able to think like Herblock and draw like Walt Kelly.
Hugh Haynie (c. 1952) remark to prospective employer.

This little, dirty cartoonist tried to make it look like I didn't visit with the President...He's at liberty to draw filthy, nasty, smear cartoons. Don't expect to get the truth from them.
Former Governor A. B. Chandler of Kentucky, quoted by *The Louisville Times* on 7 May 1963.

John Kay, Esq. of Edinburgh occupied himself as a barber for twenty-five years before turning successfully to caricature in 1784. Andre Gill, celebrated French master of the *portrait charge* during the 1870s, got his start making death masks during a cholera epidemic. Hugh Haynie was born into the feed and fertilizer business, heir to a family fishing concern originally known as the Reedville Oil and Guano Company. (It is probably just as well not to attach too much importance to this sort of insight. This writer once — in deadly student earnest — asked Walt Kelly why Pogo was a possum. Kelly's response was broken down into a number of carefully articulated, completely convincing arguments, capped by the wistful reflection that "on the other hand, he could always have been a rabbit.")

Hugh Smith Haynie was born 6 February 1927 at Reedville, a tiny coastal village in Northumberland County, Virginia. This protuberance juts into

Chesapeake Bay halfway between Washington and Norfolk. His father headed a menhaden fishing company, founded by his grandfather, which operated proudly under the slogan "Father & Son Since '81." The Haynies had been fishing the Tidewater area for eight or nine generations, right back to Captain John Haynie, whose difficulties with the Cromwell government were mentioned at the outset.

The first John Haynie might have hailed from Northumberland, England; he is supposed to have helped name the county of Virginia where he settled between 1644 and 1650. Nobody to date, however, has had any luck finding another branch of the family that spelled the name as he did. Before his death in 1685 he served variously as Burgess, King's Attorney, surveyor, justice, and captain of militia during Indian hostilities in 1677. His son, also Captain John Haynie, had the distinction in 1695 of losing, expensively, what may have been the country's first horse race. The winning mount was named Smoker; the reported stakes were a county tobacco crop and forty shillings to boot. Thereafter, the Haynies were deeply into fish. That is, until Hugh.

Haynie attended public school in Reedville, then enlisted (1944) in the U. S. Coast Guard at 17, and devoted a number of months to comparatively tranquil Pacific duty. He entered the College of William and Mary at Williamsburg in the fall of 1946 and emerged with a B.A. in Fine Arts four years later. A key exhibit you are not about to see in this anthology is his first published cartoon, which appeared 21 October 1947 on the sports page of the undergraduate paper, *The Flat Hat.* Haynie's sports cartoons were thought by some at the time to show certain points of similarity with the widely syndicated work of Thomas Paprocki, who signed himself "Pap." The latter habitually concentrated on a powerful action portrait of some hero, supported by a couple of comic vignettes. "Pap" specialized in strong, beautifully composed designs, imaginative use of borders, and flat, two-dimensional spaces that tended to keep everything to the foreground — characteristics which well might have hit a responsive chord.

The first known Haynie political cartoon appeared 9 March 1948, once again in *The Flat Hat.* It concerned President Truman, Henry Wallace, and the approaching national campaign. Growing up, Haynie's principal exposure in this field had been to the work of Fred O. Seibel, whose sparkling traditional penwork, conservative viewpoint, and inquisitive mascot "Moses Crow" had been distinguishing features of the Richmond *Times-Dispatch* since 1926. Upon graduation from college in 1950, Haynie went to work for the *Times-Dispatch* as staff artist, photo retouch man, and occasional illustrator. He recalls, with all the enthusiasm Andre Gill must have felt for his cholera death masks, happy hours spent minimizing the eccentricities of engagement portraits. During this period Haynie acquired experience in life drawing at the Richmond Professional Institute that reinforced the art history, painting, perspective, and sketching "from the antique" he had absorbed at William and Mary.

Under the tension of Korean hostilities, Haynie reentered the Coast Guard, accepted a commission, and spent much of 1951 and 1952 on weather patrol in the choppy waters of the North Atlantic. He returned to the *Times-Dispatch* as assistant editorial cartoonist with the responsibility for relieving Fred Seibel one day a week. The only tangible legacy of this brief apprenticeship may be the habit, which Haynie appears to have borrowed from Seibel, of closing and locking his studio when the daily cartoon is in progress. Seibel long practiced the custom, a particularly brave and original notion in a profession where the cartoonist's office generally is regarded as a communal ashtray.

After a short second tenure in Richmond, Haynie was informed officially he would never make it as an editorial cartoonist. He took this gentle nudge as an indication it was time to move on, and did so, to the *Greensboro Daily News,* where he was welcomed to draw on a fulltime basis. In North Carolina from 1953 to 1958 (save for a short stint on the *Atlanta Journal),* Haynie was given the freedom to make, as he put it, "mistakes, friends and, I hope, progress." Through the fifties his figures tended to take on pneumatic voluptuousness. A special feeling for calligraphy, verse, costume drama, and history developed early. Notwithstanding his family background (conservative Republicans and "Byrd" Democrats) or possibly because of it, Haynie evolved philosophically into a skeptical, fiercely independent liberal. Not only did he manage, now and again, to "think like Herblock,"

there was also for a time an unmistakeable stylistic homage, which can be seen on the wane in the opening pages of the present collection. This took the form of a fondness for splayed fingers, radial creases at elbows and knees, crayon tone-work, and regular guest appearances by the battered, middle-echelon bureaucrat who serves Herblock as Mr. Everyman.

Grover Page, cartoonist of *The Courier-Journal* since March 1919, died 5 August 1958. On 15 October the paper announced the appointment of Hugh Haynie, aged thirty-one, as his successor. Haynie's first Louisville cartoon appeared 11 December, accompanied by an editorial which welcomed "his red-headed energy and imagination" to the page:

> We wanted a man with a knowledge of art and an individual style. We were looking for a man who could bring genuine humor to his work, as well as vigor and bite. ... Many of our readers may disagree at times with the point of a Haynie cartoon. ... We believe, however, that readers will soon come to appreciate why [he] has been hailed as the most talented and promising of the young crop of American cartoonists.

The perceptive British cartoonist, Sir David Low, remarked in 1932 that the integrity of a caricaturist was a consideration of some importance: "His medium can be one of the most potent agencies for the propagation of ideas; but it, perhaps most of all such agencies, is subject to degradation." ("Low's pencil is not only not servile, it is essentially mutinous," muttered Winston Churchill in 1931. "You cannot bridle the wild ass of the desert, still less prohibit its natural hee-haw.") Given the confidence of his new employers, and a completely congenial editorial policy, Haynie bloomed. "I can honestly say that I don't believe any cartoonist in the country has more freedom than I have," he told *Newsweek* in March 1962. "In a way it's a curse. It's up to you to do something that's worthwhile."

His continuing curse. Haynie has often been called a bleeder and an agonizer. He appears perpetually dissatisfied with himself and with his efforts, not to mention his raw material. He fusses and fulminates. In 1963 a dazed interviewer found himself constantly interrupting to inquire "What are you so damn angry about?" Haynie describes the birth of a cartoon as "a process of distillation that takes intangible ideas to the tangible picture. ... You come down from Mount Olympus to Alice in Wonderland — subject, depiction, boom!" Boom! indeed.

During his first four years on *The Courier-Journal,* the new man sharpened his cutting edge and perfected his highly individual mix of Spartan design and ornate, painstakingly-wrought technique. Already much noticed in Greensboro, he continued at Louisville to attract national and international attention in steadily increasing amounts. The welcoming editorial had called attention to Haynie's "vigor," and in fact his manner and outlook contained many elements of style particularly in tune with the spirit of John Kennedy's "New Frontier." (Perhaps the most moving cartoon

in this book [p. 126] is the one of 22 November 1967: "Once Upon a Time, When I Was Very Little — And You Weren't Even Born — There Lived a Magic President...")

At a time when some of the slap and dash of contemporary crazes in the finer arts are finding their way into the editorial cartoon, Haynie nurtures a deep respect for materials and method. No matter how starkly abstract the composition, his people are standing on solid ground. To see him *really* angry, one wants to be around when a drawing comes back from an exhibition with one of his internal captions repositioned to suit the convenience of the exhibitor. If another cartoonist produces a similar idea on the same day, or worse yet, a day earlier, Haynie suffers acutely and is apt to get off a totally superfluous note assuring the other man that the overlap was an accident.

He is a bundle of paradoxes; a gracious, gregarious Virginia gentleman who answers his office phone with a ferocious "YES?" guaranteed to put all but the hardiest intruders to instant flight. He is something of a dandy; a fastidious dresser whose passion for order is reflected everywhere but in his studio; an accomplished and delightful raconteur whose tall tales are splendidly acted out in a manner that is both outrageous and courtly. Romp and Circumstance. Poet and Craftsman.

Hugh Haynie is a transitional figure. ("Aren't we all?" I can hear him say.) He has played a key role in the revitalization of the American editorial cartoon that has taken place during the sixteen years covered by this book. Haynie can have no clear notion of the esteem in which he is held by the new crop of cartoonists, many of whom were in elementary school when John Kennedy was inaugurated. His contribution has done much to break through the old perimeters, to make his calling yet more exciting and less predictable.

Haynie would not have much patience with this sort of grand summation. To him, the battles keep coming up one day at a time and the war is never over. Every cartoon is a new struggle to be fought each day between dawn and dusk. David Low liked to remember an inspirational piece of plaster statuary in the office of an editor at the *Sydney Bulletin,* during the wild frontier days of Australian journalism. It showed a taut demonic form being hauled, tail first, from an infernal pit. The inscription on the pedestal read: *Look! We've got it out again!*

Draper Hill
Memphis, Tennessee

The Eisenhower Years

"My position on this subject is perfectly clear."
29 January 1959

"I must say — that's a helluva way to run a country."

24 February 1959

With television rapidly becoming our chief information source, the older, more personal campaign methods fade into the background, and are replaced by a technology which rewards appearance.

Hugh Haynie
The Courier-Journal

"So — what else is new?"
30 January 1959

The last year of Eisenhower's administration is marked by a preoccupation with the economy. Rising inflation justifies such moves, but for a nation embroiled in a cold war with Russia, budget cuts, especially in the military, seem to jeopardize the security of a comfortable lifestyle.

"Crazy! Like why don't you cats settle down?"
12 March 1959

**"There! I knew we could all get in—
By the way, who's driving?"**

3 April 1959

Ideologies seldom split geographically in half, but in the late 1950s the major powers face off East to West. The East, under Khrushchev's monolithic direction, holds together rather nicely. The West, on the other hand, subject to obstacles such as freedom of choice, stumbles along with minimal cooperation or direction.

'A house divided against itself cannot stand'......cannot endure permanently, half slave and half free.

ABRAHAM LINCOLN
1809-1865

Hope
12 February 1959

The United States in these times feels itself to be the savior of the free world, the wrench in the cogs of the Soviet master plan. It is an attitude that will lead us into conflicts in many corners of the globe.

Pilgrim's Progress
31 March 1959

"Relax, comrade — we true revolutionaries ain't leaving."

20 July 1960

Khrushchev is seen, with some accuracy, throughout the 50s and 60s as a ruthless aggressor in all parts of the world. He begins an alliance that will plague the United States for many years to come.

"What communist squeeze?"
5 May 1960

"Dash it all, man! Can't you do something about that nutty brother of yours?"
16 June 1959

"It's a mouse — Now, it's Super-Ike!"
10 August 1959

Eisenhower's presence at the summit has given him the rosy glow of power. Although nothing really has been accomplished, Americans revere those who live in the rarefied air of statesmen like Adenauer, MacMillan and DeGaulle.

"Remember! Don't fire till they see the whites of your teeth."
13 August 1959

"I must say you've picked a helluva time to invite company."
18 August 1959

The summit conference with Khrushchev is arranged finally after months of planning. He prepares to come at a time of hectic legislative quarrels and crises for Eisenhower.

All the King's Men
11 May 1960

In May of 1960, an Air Force U-2 reconnaissance jet is shot down as it takes high-altitude photographs of the Soviet Union. The pilot, Francis Gary Powers, is subsequently tried and convicted of spying. Eisenhower takes the blame for the operation. The whole issue of presidential "insulation" will arise again when Richard Nixon becomes implicated in domestic spying operations.

"This may look silly, but it's traditional to come in this way."
1 March 1960

The beginnings of legislative hassles on the Civil Rights Bill are visible. The filibuster is used successfully for three years to delay and defeat civil rights proposals. Lyndon Johnson's candidacy for president in 1960 just happens to coincide with old friend and civil rights nemesis Sam Rayburn's decision to unshackle the Civil Rights Bill from the House Rules Committee.

"I'm comin', chile, Hallelujah! De spirit moved me!"
10 January 1960

"Oh, it's a great act — But can he ride it to the White House?"
17 February 1960
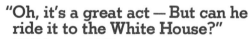
Four Democrats are in line for the party's nomination in 1960: Hubert Humphrey, Lyndon Johnson, Adlai Stevenson, and John Kennedy.

31 January 1959

"Darndest race I've ever seen."

23 May 1960

Kennedy emerges after the New Hampshire primary as the front runner, and he eventually wins the nomination. He picks Lyndon Johnson as his running mate.

The front runner

7 April 1960

HAIL! NOBLE STATESMAN...

THE GREATEST...THE FINEST...THE BEST...

FIRST IN WAR...FIRST IN PEACE...

FIRST IN THE HEART OF PROSPERITY!

BUT...OF COURSE... I WILL...

IMPROVE ALL THAT.

29 January 1960

Richard Nixon coasts to the Republican nomination with Eisenhower's personal endorsement. Major opposition comes from the party wings, led by Barry Goldwater and Nelson Rockefeller.

"Gee, it's pretty! But, of course, it hasn't been worn much."

18 March 1960

"The quarterback's hit! He laterals to the coach..."
20 October 1960

"And in conclusion, Pat and I, you know, well, we stand firmly on these issues."
1 November 1960

"For lo, the dog-days cometh and the hot air doth encompass our land."

4 August 1960

The 1960 campaign offers the nation's voters a clear choice: Kennedy is a liberal Democrat, a Roman Catholic, and a member of a wealthy Eastern family. Nixon is a veteran politician of humble origins, a Quaker, and a conservative Republican.

"The state of that Union Suit's just dandy, if I do say so m'self."

15 January 1961

Kennedy, largely because of an attractive television appearance and an unbesmirched political record, is elected by a narrow margin.

The Kennedy Years

The man and the challenge
10 November 1960

"Death to Liberal Legislation!"

HOUSE RULES COMM. POWER

"So? Let him come. I ain't going nowhere."
21 December 1960
The new, hustling president discovers early that his liberal programs, under the banner of the New Frontier, fare badly at the hands of a conservative Congress.

**Periscope off the ultra-starboard
bow.**
1 May 1961

"Axe!"
1 March 1962

12 October 1961

An eye for an eye, a tooth for a tooth, extinction for a civilization.

18 September 1961

Our mistrust of Russia after World War II has grown even greater as the Soviets perfect an awesome atomic arsenal.

"The time has come," the Walrus said, "to talk to many lands; of atom tests — and all the rest — and uninspected bans."

29 November 1961

8 March 1961

Chinese egg-roll
14 April 1961

The events that lead to our bitter involvement in Southeast Asia begin, as the United States keeps a careful eye on Chinese and North Vietnamese infiltration into Laos.

Casualties
4 April 1961

The United States, pledging support for any democratic government in Cuba, urges Castro to cut his ties with Communism. At the same time, the Cuban Revolutionary Council, headquartered in Florida, calls for the overthrow of Castro by force. Not long afterward there is an invasion of Cuba by anti-Castro forces, but Castro's militiamen wipe out the insurgent army. Later it is learned that American intelligence organizations helped train the anti-Castro troops, and engineered the ill-fated assault.

"I dare you to try a rescue."

23 August 1962

The ideological split between East and West is made tangible as East Berlin builds a nine-foot wall between its own sector and West Berlin, cutting the city in half.

Kennedy Contemplating the Bust of McCormack
20 November 1961

**Kennedy and Congress
Departing for the Chase**
12 January 1962

East Side Story
26 June 1962

The Red Chinese prepare for a supposed invasion by Nationalist Chinese by building up arms in Fukien Province, opposite the islands of Quemoy and Matsu. The United States is bound by treaty to defend Formosa in case of war, but it hedges on whether the pledge also covers Quemoy and Matsu.

"But aren't you the one who called me an appeaser yesterday?"
19 March 1962

15 May 1962

The United States wades deeper into total involvement in Vietnam.

" 'Course, I'm prepared — Just in case an updraft sweeps me up to higher altitudes."
29 September 1961

Richard Nixon seeks the office of governor in California, with the office of president in the back of his mind. This connection with the losing presidential campaign of 1960 insures his defeat.

"If YOU just hadn't fumbled, I would've won."
29 March 1962

Algerian still life: The peace table

8 March 1962

The OAS, a rightist organization pledged to keeping Algeria French, begins a terrorism and kidnapping rampage against DeGaulle's government.

Pillbox on the Maginot Line

23 January 1962

6 July 1962
President Kennedy attempts to strengthen the traditional Atlantic community of allies. The arms race and nuclear testing become the issues of discord between the Western Alliance nations and DeGaulle, who prefers to remain friendly but aloof.

"I'll thank you to keep my nose out of your business."
22 June 1962

"You and your holier-than-thou attitude!"
11 April 1962

"But, dear boy! It's so, so — dreadfully common."
15 January 1962

**"History must prove us right —
or there may be no history."**
24 October 1962

U.S.-Russian hostility reaches a climax in
the fall of 1962. President Kennedy, in a
move which causes the world to hold its
breath, orders the Russians to remove
nuclear missiles from the island of Cuba.
After tense moments, the Russians comply,
at least enough to reduce the possibility of
armed confrontation.

**"Left-right-left-right — You know
I haven't left — right!"**
15 November 1962

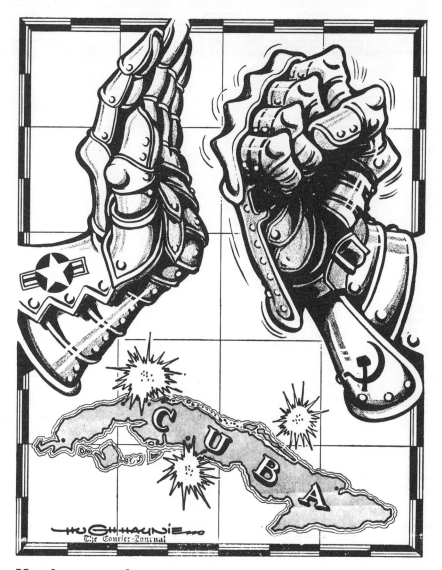

Hands across the sea
23 October 1962

"O wad some pow'r the giftie gie us, to see oursels as the whole world sees us."

8 May 1963

The first in a series of long, hot summers of civil rights violence begins. The once nonviolent movement is shouldered aside by extremists on left and right. Kennedy's attempts at legislation are defeated by a Congress with many Dixiecrats in its ranks.

Academic hood
23 September 1962

Fourscore and twenty years ago
12 February 1963

"Once again the safari enters the dense bush country."
6 January 1963

"And there she is — M-M-Miss Fortune of 1962."
10 September 1962

"It is a far, far better thing that I do..."
27 February 1963

" 'Twas all a ghastly mistake! Can you ever forgive me?"
28 February 1963

Fearing a recession, Kennedy introduces a tax plan that will include a tax cut and tax reforms. When defeat of the bill seems likely, Kennedy moves to eliminate the loophole-plugging aspect of the bill, in order to save the other half.

Long night's journey into day
18 September 1963

Civil rights violence flares in the South, following peaceful integration attempts in Birmingham, Alabama.

"Mine eyes have seen the glory,
the sorrow and the joy."
29 August 1963

"Don't get uppity with me, boy! Y'know we don't serve no presidents here."
8 June 1963

**"Kind sir, why did that donkey...
sir?"**
26 June 1963

**East side, west side, all around
the jobs**
25 July 1963

"Ladies first, buster."
8 July 1963

"But I've been sittin' in for a whole one!"
19 October 1963

"Look away! Look away! Look away to Dixie Land!"
24 October 1963

"Gee, thanks mister."
30 October 1963

Kennedy's Civil Rights Bill passes, but after being weakened almost beyond recognition.

The loneliest job
The loneliest man
The loneliest moments
10 August 1963
On the death of Patrick Bouvier Kennedy.

"H-H-H-He's already got one foot out of the grave!"
5 August 1963

The presidential hopefuls begin to line up.

"Now, really! If I planned to make the plunge, would I dress like this?"
3 March 1963

American troops move into South Vietnam to support Diem's government. The reaction at home is less than enthusiastic.

"I'll have barbecued Buddhist, tossed American greenbacks, buttered bankrolls and a glass of foreign aid."
9 October 1963

"I wish I could hide," moaned Dr. Jekyll.
12 September 1963

"But, please, no cracks about eating you-know-what."

26 October 1963

The United States sells surplus corn and other grains to Communist-bloc countries at a total cost of $250 million.

" 'Boo!' yourself."
6 November 1963

22 September 1963

C-C-COLD W-W-WAR

TENSION

GOT YOU ALL

DOUBLED-UP?

THEN DOUBLE YOUR PLEASURE! DOUBLE YOUR FUN! WITH A DOUBLE-GOOD, DOUBLE-K, DOUBLE-MOON RUN!

God Bless you, Mr. President.
The Courier-Journal H.M.

24 November 1963

On 22 November 1963, John F. Kennedy is assassinated. Lyndon Johnson, the vice-president, is sworn in as the 36th president.

23 November 1963

The Courier-Journal

BARRY BINGHAM
Editor and Publisher

LISLE BAKER
Executive Vice-President

SATURDAY, NOVEMBER 23, 1963. FOUNDED 1826.

Editorial Page Staff: RUSSELL BRINEY, Editorial Page Editor
ADELE BRANDEIS   MOLLY CLOWES
WELDON JAMES   JOHN ED PEARCE   WILLIAM PEEPLES
HUGH HAYNIE, Cartoonist

JOHN F. KENNEDY
1917-1963

PRESIDENT KENNEDY is dead, in the forty-sixth year of his life and the third of his presidency. A stunned and grieving nation cannot, at once, assess the reasons why.

John Kennedy came upon the national scene in a time of change. The face of our world was altering all around us, the temper of our nation was changing in ways not always understandable. The greatest gift he brought us was the gallantry with which he met that spirit of change, the earnestness with which he sought the ways of peace abroad and at home.

The makeshifts and compromises of the post-war era were falling apart when he became President. He had to chart new lines, to watch for new currents, to make us aware of aspirations still unmet and wrongs neglected too long.

At home and abroad the obstacles to progress were dismaying in their magnitude. But to a man of intelligence and humanity the sicknesses which beset our body politic, the rancors that divide Americans into glaring, hostile camps were evils to be overcome at all costs, even, as it turned out, at the cost of life itself.

The years and the energies of John Kennedy's presidency were dedicated to an effort to bind up the wounds of his world and his time, to heal the divisions that separate man from man. He sought an easing of tensions within the world community, the creation of an atmosphere in which East and West could grope their way toward understanding and an avoidance of nuclear holocaust. He sought within his nation a middle ground on which labor and management could meet for the economic welfare of both. And he sought to touch within the hearts of men a charity and a decency that would permit man to live with his fellow man.

He was a strong man, impetuous and given to the occasional outbursts of temper that mark strong men. His feeling for the right phrase, his articulateness and the saving note of wry gaiety which saved his occasional rhetoric from any pomposity have been matched in our time only by Franklin Roosevelt.

Underlying this surface grace and humanity of utterance was an intellectual courage, a moral toughness that made him respected in his own country and by the world at large. His words were heeded even by those who disagreed with them. His willingness to take desperate risks for peace impressed men who had earlier questioned the force of our will for peace. The epitaph history will write must take account of these facts and the progress he had made, as it will note the sacrifice demanded of him in the end.

Stunned by his death, the nation must now face the awesome questions that such a calamity poses. Shall we continue to try to heal the wounds of the world? Are we capable of the tolerance and patience and intellect that the search for peace demands? Can we honor the concepts of dignity and decency and brotherhood on which our nation was founded? Or shall we be sacrificed, as our President has been sacrificed, on the altar of man's refusal to live with man?

Of the new President, taking office under circumstances so tragic, one may say the nation is fortunate that his experience is wide, his goals are those for which President Kennedy fought and that he has the courage to walk the high and lonely path his predecessor has marked out. May God be with him.

The Johnson Years

"Out yonder we're gonna build us a Great Society!" said Lyndon Boone.

9 January 1964

U.S. POSITION IN VIETNAM
NEW VIET GOVT
McNAMARA
LBJ
LODGE
HUGH HAYNIE
The Courier-Journal

"Obviously, this situation remains somewhat fluid and murky."

31 January 1964

The United States has been involved at least peripherally in Southeast Asia for several years, but in what capacity or to what extent no one really knows. Obviously, it is an area of some hostility, though, and, in our missile-consciousness, we look at the East with great apprehension.

And the star of the East stood over where the child lay.

27 December 1963

The Russian-built Berlin Wall, completed in 1961, comes to symbolize to the free world the worst features of a totalitarian government. To the United States, which had such an important role in the fate of Germany after the war, the wall is an especially aggravating piece of masonry. Antagonism toward the Russians grows with every report of an East Berliner shot to death fleeing to freedom.

Hugh Haynie
The Courier-Journal

30 January 1964

The Bobby Baker scandal is still a hot issue, and Republicans use it to kick off their quests for the nomination. Richard Nixon and Barry Goldwater are the chief contenders.

"Watch out for Lyndon — he's tricky."
3 March 1964

O, hear the new Goldwarbler! Of victory he sings...

Right... Moderate... Moderight...

But, hark! I saw a Dickeybird... A'waiting in the wings!

HUGH HAYNIE

The Courier-Journal

10 June 1964

"You're going to lie down and rest, aren't you, Barry?...Barry!"
5 May 1964

15 July 1964
Barry Goldwater is the GOP choice.

"By golly! It does feel good!"

1 June 1964

Cloture stops the Dixiecrat filibuster of the
Civil Rights Bill, and its subsequent passage
offers hope to a nation that is weary of
civil rights disorders.

Pied Piper of the ghettos

28 July 1964

Hope is short-lived, however, as the summer brings renewed violence across the nation. Riots, the worst so far, erupt in New York, Rochester, and Philadelphia.

"W-W-Well, shut mah mouf-f-f!"

11 June 1964

"Look, Jack! They passed it!"
20 June 1964

Brave legends never die
6 April 1964

Gen. Douglas MacArthur, commander of
the Pacific theatre in World War II, dies.

25 January 1965

Winston Churchill dies at age 90.

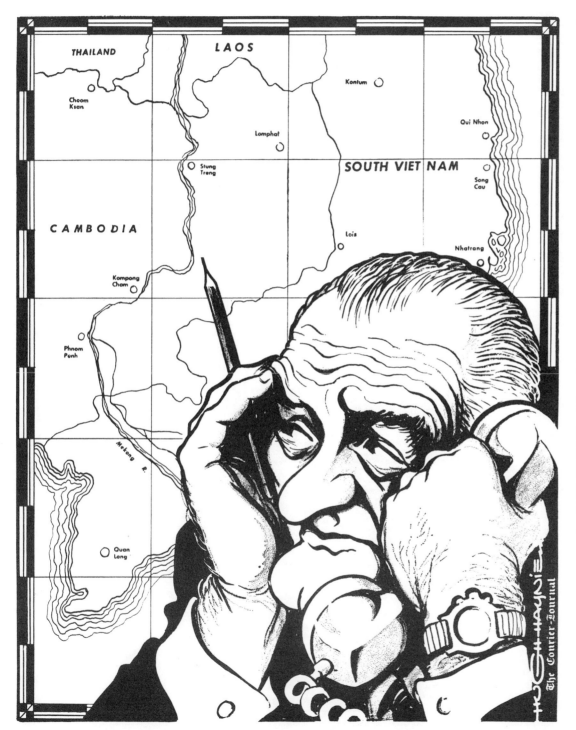

"May I speak to our staunch, loyal ally, the head of the South Vietnamese government — whoever it is today."
5 September 1964

"Damn the torpedoes! Full speed ahead! We have just begun to fight!"
5 August 1964

President Johnson cements our commitment to South Vietnam. Speculation about the wisdom of his judgment arises due to the shaky Vietnamese government we are pledging to support.

"Liberty in the definition of extremism is no vice."
12 August 1964

"Mommy, why are the other kids 'fraid to play with me?"

9 September 1964

Barry Goldwater, the Republican nominee, and Lyndon Johnson, the Democratic choice, begin the presidential campaign. Johnson seems to be a shoo-in from the start, and Goldwater undermines his own credibility with statements about the availability of nuclear weapons to NATO field commanders.

"Look! We're climbing higher on the polls every minute!"
26 October 1964

"You're getting confident...very confident...overconfident..."
5 October 1964

"Verily I say unto thee, thou shalt be delivered out of the wilderness and unto the promised landslide."

4 March 1965

This bit of prophecy follows the disastrous Republican campaign.

"— And the elephant, too?"

9 November 1964

Johnson, running virtually a non-campaign, wins in a landslide.

"Come on, fella — get off my back."

30 April 1965

Revolution rocks the government of the Dominican Republic in a coup led by Army officers supporting the return of exiled President Juan Bosch. U.S. Navy destroyers evacuate 2,300 Americans from Santo Domingo. U.S. Army and intelligence personnel are said to have been responsible for the defeat of the coup, which would have restored Bosch, a Castro-backed Communist, to power. Our intrusion into a foreign civil war conjures visions of "gunboat diplomacy" and triggers criticism at home.

Teddy Johnson and the era of big-stick diplomacy.

4 May 1965

"If you love me, how come you never take me anywhere?"
26 June 1965

The dark at the top of the escalator
4 August 1965

The first real troop detachment is sent to Vietnam. Nine thousand Marines comprise the initial fighting unit in a theatre that eventually involves millions of American soldiers.

" 'Course we're not trying to hide
anything! Now — if you look
right here..."
19 November 1965

"A funny thing happened on my way to the Great Society Ball."
11 January 1966

12 February 1966

"When I first picked this up, I had no idea it went on and on and on and on."

7 March 1966

"I don't think y'all realize it, but everybody's out of step but me!"

15 June 1966

America looks to her Western allies for help in Vietnam, but none seem to want to share in the dubious glory of international intrusion.

"Latest intelligence reports...

indicate no real hope for...

a permanent cease-fire...

here in the United States."

29 December 1965

"I haven't really lost touch with you — the people — have I?"
25 May 1966

"You ought to come back and help us fix it! Someday even You may need a boat."

24 March 1966

DeGaulle announces his plans to remove French Army officers from NATO forces. At the same time he wishes to remain a part of the NATO alliance.

"Y'know Charlie, for a friend, you're an awful pain in the neck."

27 February 1966

"Yep, it's nice to be winning the space race — too bad we're still losing the human one."
14 September 1966

"Black Power!"
5 July 1966

The orderly civil rights movement crumbles under the fiery speeches of Stokely Carmichael, Rap Brown, and others. Often, this early display of black nationalism leads to extremist violence and white backlash.

On the tombstone: GOP 1854-1964 RIP

"Koochie — koochie — koo!"

10 November 1966

The GOP, buried in the last presidential
election, wins virtually across-the-board
in nationwide congressional elections,
giving the first quantitative evidence of
the unpopularity of Johnson's war policy.

"They s-s-say I'll arrive s-s-sooner this way."
4 July 1966

The Age of Exploration:
Lyndon's discovery of China

19 October 1966

LBJ begins a tour of Asia, saying he would like to bury the hatchet with the Chinese. It is the first disclosure of any American desire to reach a détente.

"The little match girl lit yet another one and, lo! She saw a warm and happy Great Society. A chill wind from the East blew it out."

14 December 1966

"No! No! child — not like me!
Just be like him!"
26 December 1966

"I'll order the escalation. You issue a denial to the press. And you think up a new name for it when they find out."

23 April 1967

"So? Eve and I snitched a few lousy apples! But, if you throw me out you're anti-Negro!"

6 January 1967

Adam Clayton Powell, Democratic congressman from New York, comes under investigation for illegal travel at public expense, padding his congressional staff, and misuse of public funds. Later he is removed from office.

24 February 1967

7 April 1967

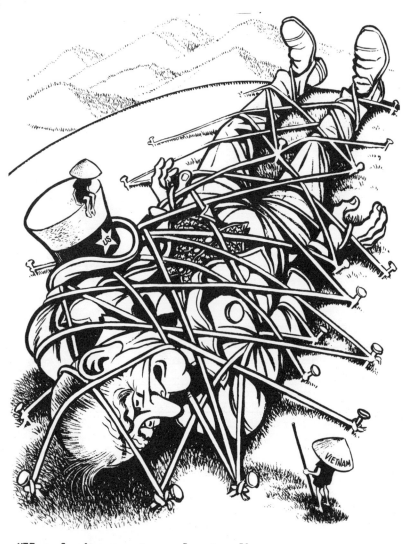

"You don't seem to understand!
I am the strongest man on
Earth!" thundered Uncle
Gulliver.
12 May 1967

"I said, 'We must (cough!) do something (wheeze!) about (snort!) air (gasp!) pollution.'"

1 February 1967

Pollution again comes to the attention of the American public. President Johnson addresses a joint session of Congress asking them to initiate strong air pollution legislation.

"Very well — Are you Jews ready to yield to my truce demands?"

9 June 1967

In the summer of 1967, the hostility between Israel and the Arab States flares into all-out war. The United States and the Soviet Union, sympathizers with Israel and Egypt, respectively, remain in the background. In the six days of fighting, Israel destroys the Arabs.

"Honey, do you think the neighbors will think we're corny if we put out the flag today?"
4 July 1967

"Kick ol' Uncle Tom in the head again, man! He's still breathin'."
1 July 1967

Riots in black communities become more severe in intensity and more sophisticated in performance. Molotov cocktails and automatic weapons augment rocks and bottles.

"You must admit, it's direct, concise and to the point."
16 July 1967

Perennial Phoenix
19 September 1967

**"Once upon a time, when I was
very little — and you weren't
even born — there lived a
magic president…"**
22 November 1967

State of the Union
18 January 1968

"You gave up the WHAT?!!"

25 January 1968

A United States ship, the Pueblo, carrying sensitive electronic gear, is captured on the high seas by North Korean patrol boats. They claim that the Pueblo is spying within their territorial waters. It is the first time in history that an American ship has been captured by an enemy during peacetime. Americans are outraged and the Navy is more than a little embarrassed.

John Paul Jones

Bony and Pride
27 March 1968

"Didn't you get the word to extinguish all (pooff!) unnecessary lights?"
16 February 1968

"...But his truth is marching on..."

5 April 1968

Dr. Martin Luther King is shot and killed in Memphis, Tennessee. Americans tense for retaliatory violence. The outcry for stricter gun control rises again, but the National Rifle Association stands ready to protect that sacred American tradition of carrying handguns and rifles.

"We're here to fill the shoes of
Martin Luther King!"
6 April 1968

"For Pete's sake, man! Don't
point that thing at me — it might
be loaded!"
1 October 1967

"Sure, I know who you are!
You're the nice man named
ruthless opportunist!"
2 May 1968

"Pack up the issues (and the
delegates) in your old kit bag
and smile! smile! smile!"
7 May 1968

"A Hubird in the hand is worth two out beating the bush."

12 May 1968

Democrats Johnson, Humphrey, Kennedy, McGovern, and McCarthy scramble for momentum before the convention.

"Howdy! Name's Goliath! Don't believe I caught yours, li'l fella."

5 December 1967

"My God! What have we become?"

6 June 1968

Sen. Robert Kennedy is shot to death while campaigning in Los Angeles.

"He was a nice man who stood up for what he believed, so somebody shot him just like his brother. I think it's called the American way of politics."
7 June 1968

"This must all be a very bad dream!" moaned Alice.

27 August 1968

The Democrats convene in Chicago.

30 August 1968

"Mayor Daley? I just had to call and congratulate you on the masterful way you slaughtered that donkey in your stockyards."

31 August 1968

Anti-war demonstrations and overly brutal reactions from Chicago police make the convention mood ugly. The actions of the police in these three days give much impetus to the anti-war movement, and the Democratic Party takes it on the chin. In the middle of this turbulence, Hubert Humphrey gets the nomination.

"Take me along! Oh, won't you take me along-g-g-g?"
12 September 1968

"Sir! I respectively request permission to go ashore, sir!"
1 October 1968

"Goodness no! I've never seen one grow THAT big!"
22 September 1968

3 October 1968

15 October 1968

"Quick! Retraction secretary!
Ol' Sper-o just made another
statement."
25 September 1968

"No! No! That fellow over there, now! Nixon's the one!"
7 November 1968

Richard Nixon wins the presidential election. Johnson gladly unshoulders the Vietnam War burden.

The Nixon Years

"But this job, like any other one, isn't too bad, once you learn the ropes."

21 November 1969

"Out, damned blot!"
12 January 1969

**"Good morning, Mr. President!
And what's on your mind today?"**

21 January 1969

President Nixon takes the oath of office at a
time of exceptional national instability and
division.

"Mammy, where did I come from?"
26 February 1969

"Wonder why grownups always have enough money for killin' and never enough for livin'?"
13 March 1969

"Where? Here? Goodness knows I can't see it."
7 February 1969

"...And in Paris today, the peace talks recessed once again with both sides still reporting no progress."

4 February 1969

Substantive peace talks between hostile nations begin in January 1969. Henry Cabot Lodge is the head of the U.S. delegation, while Gen. Nguyen Cao Ky represents South Vietnam, when he isn't skiing. Frustration is the byword of these early sessions. Progress in the early months is limited to a joint decision on what shape the negotiating table will take.

**"1984 didn't get here fast enough
for us in the 'now' generation."**
17 June 1969

Attorney General John Mitchell asserts, in a
Chicago Federal Court brief, that the
government has the power to eavesdrop
on any "subversive" group without court
supervision. But, he declares, citizens need
not fear electronic eavesdropping "unless
they are in organized crime."

**"Me? Reform? Y'mush be kiddin'!
Y'know I'm th'life of the parties!"**
7 March 1969

American know-how
17 July 1969

Man reaches the moon, a technological and transcendental giant step in the history of our planet. Many believe, though, that man would be better served by spending those billions on fulfillment of more basic human needs.

e·col'o·gy (ē·kŏl'ō·jĭ), *n.* The study of the mutual relationship between organisms and their environment.

"A few years ago I didn't know that word existed...In a few more it probably won't..."
22 April 1970

"Preposterous! Why, if we (wheeze!) complied, we'd be (gasp!) bankrupt! You (snort!) do-gooders are just (cough!) trying to choke off industry in this community!"
19 October 1969

The "great, silent majority" in concert.
28 November 1969

After a rally of 250,000 anti-war demonstrators in Washington, D. C., President Nixon remains unmoved. He defends his Vietnam policy, saying the "great silent majority" of the American people stands behind him.

Consistency
5 October 1969

With occasional peace rumors, Nixon carefully nurtures a glimmer of hope for Vietnam troop withdrawal. After a while, however, the American people begin to wonder whether Nixon's "End The War" pledge was just another campaign tactic.

Pax-art poster
16 August 1970

**"Our latest offensive should
shorten...rather than enlarge
the war and save American lives
...beyond a shadow of a doubt."**
2 May 1970

Premier Lon Nol of Cambodia appeals to
President Nixon for the intervention of
American troops in his country. After days
of deliberation, Nixon decides to involve
U.S. air and ground forces in Cambodia,
touching off a severe wave of anger and
dissent across the nation.

**"Now that I've made our position
in Vietnam crystal clear...
let us turn to Laos and
Cambodia."**
21 April 1970

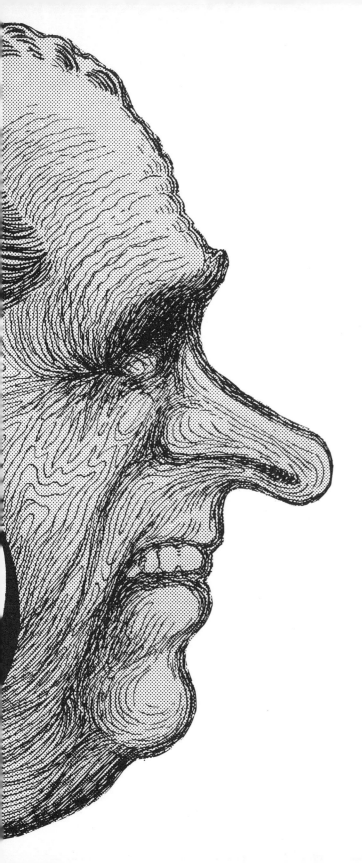

"And in the ever-widening jungle war, U.S. troops pushed forward, inflicting heavy casualties."

6 May 1970

The "student revolution," born in the mid-60s by the Vietnam War, reaches a chilling, bloody climax as four students at Kent State University are shot to death, allegedly by Ohio National Guardsmen during a student demonstration. Provocation is claimed by the soldiers, but a subsequent presidential commission suggests that the guardsmen were at fault.

"Thus Camelot, the once, and perhaps future dream, settled into the mists of Chappaquidick Island."

3 August 1969

Massachusetts Sen. Edward Kennedy, a potential candidate for the presidency in 1972, is involved in an automobile accident. Mary Jo Kopechne, one of his office staff, is drowned. Details of what happened are never fully revealed, leaving many rumors unchecked and Kennedy's political future uncertain.

"Nixon? Dump me? You've got to be kidding! Who would make the deliveries?"

30 October 1970

"Today we take on the news media! Tomorrow, the whole asylum!"

15 November 1969

"Damndest seesaw I've ever seen."

22 November 1970

Vietnam, drugs, crime, racism; none of these national problems means quite as much to the common American as the rising cost of living. The winters of discontent are sown when fractions of pennies are added on to goods and services each month, snowballing over the years to sizeable, and annoying, increases. The machinations of international finance are apparently bewildering to the common man, and Nixon's economic advisors as well.

Everybody wants to go to heaven...but nobody wants to die.

6 December 1970

**"But Army Intelligence had
informed our boys that there
were only VC troops in My Lai
...many cleverly disguised as
women, children, chickens..."**
22 December 1970

**"We must conclude that there was
a tragic massacre at My Lai by
American troops. But, thank
God, no individual soldiers
were involved."**
16 January 1971

A horrifying story of mass murder in the
Vietnam War gradually surfaces. An
American infantry patrol on a search-and-
destroy mission is said to have wiped out
every person in the village of My Lai. The
actual number of dead men, women, and
children is not known, but the Army, which
reluctantly brings charges against Lt.
William Calley and Capt. Ernest Medina,
puts the number at 103.

"But look at it this way: Have you ever tried to argue with a Jewish mother?"

19 March 1971

The United States takes on yet another peacekeeping role, this time in the Middle East. Israel refuses to give back the territory it captured from the Arabs in the Six-Day War.

"But at last I see the light at the end...

of this Indo-Chinese tunnel."
24 March 1971

Wipe...wipe...wipe...
31 March 1971

Lt. William Calley is found guilty of the premeditated murder of twenty-two Vietnamese civilians. Military law demands either life imprisonment or the death penalty, but Calley's sentence is commuted to twenty years.

"And I'll not rest until you're dead!"
9 September 1971

"All of a sudden I smell something burning."

20 June 1971

Dr. Daniel Ellsberg, a former Rand Corporation researcher, makes public a compilation of top secret memoranda, written orders, and documents, which come to be known as the Pentagon Papers. The study, originally ordered by Secretary of Defense Robert McNamara in 1968, reveals the behind-the-scenes decisions which led to deeper American involvement in Vietnam.

"Oh good grief! A matched set!"
9 July 1971

One of the incidental, but by no means minor, results of the Vietnam War is drug addiction. The easy availability of hard drugs and the depressing quality of GI life in Vietnam combine to create a problem which spills over into American life.

"Aha! Thought you had me that time, didn't you Red-ink Baron?"
9 May 1971

The Lockheed Aircraft Corporation, facing bankruptcy, is loaned $250 million by the federal government. Many believe that Lockheed, which also receives many lucrative defense contracts, has been given preferential treatment.

"Sure it's a kooky game...but at least he's wagging his tail."
14 April 1971

The United States and China, which have not had diplomatic relations with each other for twenty years, seem to be on the verge of a détente. The unlikely catalyst for this diplomatic breakthrough is the game of table tennis.

"Talk about a zoo! We're supposed to watch things like hawks — paid like churchmice — worked like mules — cussed like cats — called pigs — and then shot like dogs."
5 May 1971

Phoenix, escalating from the ashes
11 November 1971

The air war continues in Vietnam as the ground war winds down.

"Sure! I'm a lousy, rotten, crooked, selfish monster! But remember...I got YOU elected."
22 November 1971

"Now let me make the Big Picture perfectly clear..."
8 December 1971

The United States watches as her ally, Pakistan, falls before the invading Indian Army. Anti-war feeling prohibits America from taking a more aggressive role in this conflict.

"Back to the White House. And you?"   "Oh, really? Me too!"

"...ALL ABOARD...!"

"Actually, jogging's much healthier!"   "Oh, indeed! Indeed!"

12 January 1972

"Bon voyage, pinko."
6 November 1971

"It's nice to see you again, too,
after so long a time!"
21 February 1972

Military Backbone
9 April 1972

"Let us continue to prey for peace."
28 April 1972

**"Read me the results of the
Democratic primaries again..."**
20 March 1972

**"Wiiissshhh! Wiiissshhh! Wiisshh!
Wish..."**
7 May 1972

**"Oh! Ah got a bran' new pair of
roller skates..."**
14 March 1972

"...Sorry about that..."
6 April 1972

Sen. Edmund Muskie of Maine, the
Democratic front runner for months,
watches as his campaign loses momentum
and falls apart. Sen. George McGovern of
South Dakota, a fast finisher for the
Democratic nomination in 1968, emerges
as a strong candidate.

Mine number one off Haiphong harbor
10 May 1972

"Yes, I hope I remembered everything...but with weather like this, I just never know what to pack."
21 May 1972

The second half of Nixon's peace tour — balancing act takes him to Russia. Pending negotiations are clouded by the decision to mine the Haiphong harbor and prevent Russian ships from unloading supplies to the North Vietnamese.

"Awright! True Americans! Let's hear it for good ol' George... and against those pinko gun controls!"
19 May 1972

For Governor George C. Wallace... and the American political system
17 May 1972

Governor Wallace of Alabama, a candidate for the Democratic presidential nomination, is shot and wounded while campaigning in Maryland.

"Give me your tired, your poor old pols...your sulking Meany yearning to breathe fire...the wretched wreckage of your Wallace cause. Send these, the homeless, disgruntled Democrats to me..."
14 July 1972

"Remember the good ol' Chicago days when they were outside raising hell, and not inside voting?"
11 July 1972

"Hi there, fellas! Here I am! Your candidate, George McGovern!"
28 June 1972

"Now, face the camera...say... ...No, No! 'Cheese'...not 'Geez!'"
14 June 1972

George McGovern, riding a surge of anti-war feeling and support from all the minorities, is the presidential candidate for the reform-minded Democrats.

"I am sorry, but the number you have bugged is not in service at this time..."

27 June 1972

"Right on...!"

18 June 1972

"Ah ha! Welcome again to the lair of Wild Blue Yonder Beard!"

7 July 1972

Two armed hijackers seize a Pacific Southwest jet at San Francisco International Airport and demand $800,000 ransom for the 87 passengers. Federal agents kill the would-be plane pirates. This is just one of many hijacking attempts during the summer.

"And this is perhaps the weirdest little bug discovered in the Democratic party headquarters..."
5 August 1972

"I must say, you have an incredibly honest face..."
29 August 1972

Perhaps the most serious and intriguing political drama of our time begins to unfold. The office of the National Headquarters of the Democratic Party has been bugged, and the men arrested in that raid have close ties to the Committee to Re-elect the President.

"Well, so much for the left-end sweep. On 2, shift right and go up the middle."
31 August 1972

"Perhaps not 1000%...but you certainly were behind me, George."
2 August 1972

McGovern chooses Sen. Thomas Eagleton of Missouri as his vice-presidential running mate. Later it is revealed that Eagleton had received a series of shock treatments to relieve depression. In a flurry of maneuvering, the McGovern people decide that Eagleton and his problem are too heavy for their already spindly campaign to bear, and they ask him to step aside. Sargent Shriver is Eagleton's replacement.

23 September 1972

The 1972 presidential campaign is a classic of sorts, with McGovern playing Don Quixote to Nixon's windmill. The president relies on his built-in momentum to carry him through many problems, none of which seem to interest the American electorate.

"Fine! Just fine, thanks! And when do you expect to get yours rolling?"

20 September 1972

8 November 1972

"Of course I don't walk on troubled waters ... I walk OVER them!"

24 September 1972

Richard Nixon is re-elected by a staggering margin. For all its good intentions and noble aims, the McGovern campaign appeal falls on millions of deaf ears.

**"Now, just tell the folks back
home that there is absolutely
no racial discrimination aboard
this ship. Right, boy?"**
21 November 1972

Arab Olympiad
6 September 1972

One of the more grisly incidents in recent
times occurs during the summer Olympic
Games in Munich, Germany. Arab terrorists
turn this festival of brotherhood and sports
into a political battleground as they attack
the Israeli dormitory, taking nine hostages.
All are murdered later, and four of the
Palestinian attackers are killed in the airport
shoot-out.

"The Saturday Evening Post...
Collier's...Look...and now, I've
managed to kill this, itself!"
9 December 1972

"The answer, my friend, is
blowing up to win! The answer
is blowing up to win...!"
21 December 1972

"Hey, guys! It's ol' chrome-dome Samson! He wants his (heh! heh!) hair back."
14 January 1973

"Thou mayest announce to the assembled multitudes that my governmental reorganization is complete."
17 December 1972

"And next, I'd like to introduce my friend, what's-his-name, who will be my new Secretary of Something-or-other."
14 December 1972

"Yoo-hoo, Mr. Nixon! Where am I...really...?"
11 March 1973

"These socialistic boondoggles are no panacea, boy! The simple solution to your poverty is to get rich!"
8 February 1973

"First in war, first in peace, first in the pockets of my countrymen!"
31 January 1973

"Quick! Tell the White House that the truth is leaking out of the durn Watergate."
17 January 1973

"Okay, fellow bugs...be very careful what you tell them! Remember: BIG BUG IS WATCHING YOU!"
9 February 1973

The Senate Select Committee on Presidential Campaign Activities is appointed to investigate the Watergate break-in and the alleged cover-up.

The law-and-order Administration. The administration of law-and-order.
23 April 1973

**"One little, two little, three from Watergate...
...four little, five little, six... incarcerate...
seven little...WAIT!"**
1 February 1973

The list of Administration and Committee to Re-elect the President staffers implicated through the Watergate investigations begins to reach labyrinthine proportions.

"My God! Is there no cure for a bleeding Ulster...?"

6 February 1973

Nine people are killed, and fifteen are wounded as Protestant and Roman Catholic gunmen raid each others' sections of Belfast, spraying machine gun bullets from speeding cars. It is one of the bloodiest nights in Northern Ireland since fighting broke out anew in 1969.

"Return to your tepee, my good man...content in the knowledge that you've smoked the peace pipe with honor!"

10 May 1973

Two hundred militant members of the American Indian movement surrender the town of Wounded Knee, South Dakota, to federal marshals, ending a violent, seventy-day protest over unsatisfactory treatment of Indians by the government.

"Boy, that poor ol' elephant sure has a sloppy track ahead of him."

17 July 1973

"I repeat: We demand a closer look at you, Watergate Monster!"

15 March 1973

President Nixon makes a policy statement on executive privilege, saying members of his personal staff would refuse to testify before congressional committees.

"Well, some of us can walk on Watergate and some others can't...pity..."

27 March 1973

President Nixon withdraws his nomination of L. Patrick Gray as permanent director of the FBI, following confirmation hearings in which Gray said, with unexpected frankness, that the FBI knew of Herbert Kalmbach's payments to Donald Segretti for his political sabotage campaigns, and that he personally had turned over transcripts of wiretapped conversations to John Dean.

"But it's high time you come clean in the Watergate, children!" said Mary Poppins, ascending.
19 April 1973

"Please! Mr. Nixon...I'm asking in a nice way...OPEN THE DOOR!"
15 April 1973

"WHAT Watergate cover-up?"
28 April 1973

"Help! My name is National
Security and I'm being
threatened!"
1 June 1973

"Cover-up, bosh! Don't you Yanks
have any bloomin' imagination?"
5 June 1973

"...The whole truth and nothing
but the..."
3 June 1973

"Flushed with his stunning victory at Windmill-on-Watergate, Don Nixote sallied forth to challenge the inflationary dragon."

14 June 1973

"My God! I'm on the White House 'Enemy List'!"

28 June 1973

Watergate investigators learn of the existence of a White House "Enemy List," which includes the names of politicians, writers, businessmen and entertainers opposed to Richard Nixon.

"HELP STAMP OUT JOHN DEAN!"

20 June 1973

"Well, suh! This jus' might unravel the mummy's secret!"

18 July 1973

The Senate Committee learns of taped conversations between Nixon and members of his staff, including Ehrlichman and Haldeman.

"It is my understanding that they went to feather the nests at San Clemente and Key Biscayne."

1 July 1973

Richard Nixon's personal finances begin to be scrutinized. It is learned that the government spent $703,000 on improvements at his private homes.

24 July 1973

Tapes? Schnapes!

NIXXON

"We'd like you to know... absolutely nothing!"

CHUCK HAYNIE
© 1973 The Courier-Journal

"Get a good lawyer, hell! I AM a good lawyer, as is my personal attorney here!"
21 July 1973

President Nixon refuses to release tapes to either the Senate Committee, special prosecutor Archibald Cox, or Judge John Sirica, in spite of orders from the U.S. Court of Appeals.

"I'm O.K. You're O.K."

8 August 1973

The firestorm of investigations in Washington quickly switches to Vice-President Spiro Agnew. Evidence will be presented to a Baltimore Federal Grand Jury outlining extensive political corruption on his part, going back to his days as governor of Maryland.

**Watergate, Watergate, everywhere,
nor any drop to drink;
Watergate, Watergate, everywhere,
and lo, the heads did shrink.**

5 August 1973

**Latest white paper on the
Watergate scandal**

17 August 1973

"Would you buy a used country
from this man?"
28 August 1973

"I shall not, I shall not be moved!"
26 September 1973

"Your problem, Spiro, is that you've become a dirty White-Household word."
19 September 1973

20 September 1973
The White House conspicuously avoids supporting Vice-President Spiro Agnew while he is investigated. Eventually he resigns, and pleads no contest to a charge of income tax evasion.

"Head for the oval office, Dickey!
They can't corner you there!"
28 October 1973

4 November 1973

From ghoulies and ghosties ✝✝✝ and long-leggety IMPEACHMENTS and things that go BUG in the night, ❀ good lawyers, deliver us! ✝✝✝

"Tilt, indeed! One more peep out of you, sister, and YOU'RE fired!"

16 November 1973

Special prosecutor Archibald Cox persists in his efforts to obtain the White House tapes, and is fired by President Nixon. Deputy Attorney General William Ruckelshaus is dismissed, and Attorney General Elliot Richardson resigns. Both refuse to fire Cox under orders. This extreme action by the president spurs impeachment proceedings, some already in the works.

"Hi guys! I'm Jerry Ford, the new substitute...Gee whiz, how'd you fellas manage t'get so muddy?"
7 December 1973
Gerald Ford, Republican congressman from Michigan since 1948, and minority leader in the House since 1965, is President Nixon's choice to fill the vacant vice-presidential chair. His nomination is quickly ratified by the Congress.

20 April 1973

The Arab oil-producing nations announce an embargo of their products to pro-Israeli nations, especially the United States, the Netherlands, Japan and the Philippines. American oil producers claim that the energy crisis has been coming anyway, but this embargo signals the beginning of recognition of the world-wide shortage of fuel.

Whilst brooding over my recent misfortunes, a wee, small voice whispered to me, "Cheer up, things could be worse!" So I cheered up...and, sure enough, things got worse.

2 December 1973

"I'll bet you'd never guess who sold me this used car."
29 November 1973

"Say, you look a little rundown y'self, John! John...?"
20 December 1973

"Let there be oil! And, by the beard of the profit, let there be vast riches from the sale thereof!"
27 December 1973

"Since I'm as innocent and pure
as the driven snow...

...why should I release evidence
that makes me look guilty?"
29 December 1973

"...meooooowwww...!"

19 March 1974

Judge John Sirica orders the grand jury report on Richard Nixon's Watergate behavior be given to the House Judiciary Committee. House committee members regard this as a major step in their impeachment investigation.

"Yoo-hoo...Mr. Nixon!"

20 March 1974

Everyone in Washington, save Richard Nixon, begins to realize that impeachment or resignation is inevitable within the year. Sen. James Buckley, conservative Republican and Nixon backer, is among those to call for his resignation. At the same time, Nixon says to a meeting of the National Association of Broadcasters that he will "stand and fight."

"His master's hmmmmmmmmmmmm."
30 March 1974

"...Meanwhile, twisting slowly,
slowly in the wind..."
12 May 1974

"Very well, surrender the crown jewels...but never the crown!"

17 May 1974

Nixon vows he'll "never give up" as the House Judiciary Committee begins its examination of the subpoenaed tapes.

"Another year older and I'm still here in Watergate. But, at least I'm still here! I'm still here!"

4 July 1974

"High crimes and misdemeanors, indeed! I won't fall for that."

18 July 1974

Former White House staffer Clark Mollenhoff testifies that Richard Nixon, through H. R. Haldeman, ordered IRS investigations of political enemies, specifically George Wallace. John Doar, the House Judiciary Committee's majority counsel, says he plans to urge the committee to recommend impeachment.

"I shall not, I shall not be removed! Just like a tree that's planted by the Watergate...!"

30 July 1974

The House Judiciary Committee adopts Article II of the impeachment proceedings, charging that Richard Nixon failed to carry out his presidential oath of office. The charges of the second article are: use of IRS files to audit political enemies, misuse of the FBI and CIA, creation of an illegal activities branch (the Plumbers), and the wiretapping of government employees and private citizens.

"...TO GO?"

7 August 1974

Nixon releases three tape transcripts which link him to the Watergate cover-up, practically from the beginning. Nixon, who admits this new information is at odds with his earlier statements, now says that his impeachment is "virtually a foregone conclusion."

9 August 1974

Richard Nixon surrenders to the over-whelming amount of impeachment evidence gathered against him and becomes the first president in United States history to resign from office. Vice-President Gerald Ford, nominated for office in October of 1973, is sworn in as president on the same day.

26 August 1974